C000076147

The Puppet Theatre

Brandon Robshaw

Published in association with
The Basic Skills Agency

Hodder & Stoughton
A MEMBER OF THE HODDER HEADLINE GROUP

Acknowledgements
Cover: Jim Eldridge
Illustrations: Jim Eldridge

Orders; please contact Bookpoint Ltd, 39 Milton Park, Abingdon, Oxon OX14
4TD. Telephone: (44) 01235 400414, Fax: (44) 01235 400454. Lines are open
from 9.00–6.00, Monday to Saturday, with a 24 hour message answering service.
Email address: orders@bookpoint.co.uk

British Library Cataloguing in Publication Data
A catalogue record for this title is available from the British Library

ISBN 0 340 77258 1

First published 2000
Impression number 10 9 8 7 6 5 4 3 2 1
Year   2005 2004 2003 2002 2001 2000

Copyright © 2000 Brandon Robshaw

Typeset by GreenGate Publishing Services, Tonbridge, Kent.
Printed in Great Britain for Hodder & Stoughton Educational, a division of
Hodder Headline Plc, 338 Euston Road, London NW1 3BH, by Atheneum
Press, Gateshead, Tyne & Wear

The Puppet Theatre

Contents

1

A Chance Find

Jenny found the puppet theatre by chance.
She wasn't looking for it.
It was in a back street,
a long way from the sea front.

The street was quiet and empty.
The building looked old and dirty.
A sign above the door said 'PUPPET
THEATRE'
in faded gold letters.

The door was ajar.
Jenny pushed it.
It swung open.
Jenny stepped out of the sunshine,
into the dark.

Inside, there was a smell of age and dust.
The carpet was soft and deep.
As her eyes got used to the dark,
Jenny saw rows and rows of seats.
At the front was a tiny stage
with red velvet curtains.

The place was dead quiet.
There was nobody about.
Jenny was about to leave.
Then she heard a slight noise.

The curtains opened just a little.
A tiny face peeped through the gap.
It had a black moustache and staring eyes.

Jenny gave a little scream.
The face was too small to be a man's.
It was ... *a puppet.*

Its mouth opened.
'What are you doing here?'
it said angrily.
'Who let you in?'

2

The General

Jenny stood frozen to the spot.

'What are you doing here?'
said the puppet again.

The curtains opened all the way.
The puppet stood in the middle of the stage.
He was about the size of a two-year-old child.
He was wearing an army uniform
with lots of medals on.

He pointed at Jenny.
'Who let you in?'
he asked angrily.

Suddenly, Jenny heard the sound of laughter.
A man stepped onto the stage.
He held the strings of the soldier puppet
in his hand.
He pulled the strings and the soldier puppet
did a little dance.

'Bet that gave you a shock!' said the man.
He was an old man with a bald head.
He had a wrinkled, mocking face,
like a monkey.

'It did give me a shock!' said Jenny.
'I nearly had a heart attack!'

'Just my little joke,' said the old man.

'This is the General.'
He pulled one of the strings
and the General bowed.
'Maybe you'd like to meet the other puppets?'
said the old man.
'I'd love to,' said Jenny.

3

Jenny Meets the Puppets

The old man went to the back of the stage
and pulled out a large box.
He took out another puppet –
a woman with grey curly hair
and a green silk dress.
She had a large, hooked nose.
'This is Lady Muck,'
said the old man.
'She's the General's wife.'
He made Lady Muck bow.

He took out another puppet.
'This is their son Johnny.'
Johnny was a handsome young man
with red cheeks and a wide smile.
He wore a soldier's uniform like his Dad,
only without medals.

The old man took out the last puppet.
It was a large hairy dog with big teeth.
'Meet Rex,' he said.
He made Rex's mouth open and shut
and said 'Woof woof!'

Jenny laughed.
'They look almost alive!'

'There used to be one more,'
said the old man.
'Johnny had a girlfriend
called Sweetheart.

She got old and worn.
Lost her looks.
I had to throw her out.
A pity.
The show's not the same without her.'

'Can't you get a new one?'
asked Jenny.

'It's not easy to find
the right sort of puppet, these days,'
said the old man.
'But I'm always on the look-out.'

'I hope you find one,' said Jenny.

'Oh, yes, I'm sure I will,'
said the old man.
He looked at Jenny and laughed.
'I think I'll find one
very soon.'

4

Tickets to the Show

'I'd better be going,' said Jenny.
'My parents will wonder where I am.'

'Are you on holiday here?'
asked the old man.

'Yes – with my Mum and Dad,'
said Jenny.
'They're down at the beach today.
But I wanted to explore the town.'

'And you found my theatre!' said the old man.
'That was a bit of luck.'
He laughed.
'Look – here's three tickets for tonight's show.
Bring the family.'

'Thanks a lot!' said Jenny. 'We'll be here.'

The old man turned to his puppets.
He picked up two in each hand
and held them by the strings.
'Did you hear that?' he said.
'There'll be people watching you tonight.
You'll put on a good show, won't you?'

The four puppets turned their heads
to look at Jenny.
Then they turned back to look at the old man.
All together, they nodded their heads.

'They really do look as if they're alive!' said
Jenny.

'See you tonight,' said the old man.

5

'Come in, come in'

Jenny's parents were surprised and pleased
when she told them about the free show.

The show started at eight o'clock.
It was still light when they left the hotel,
but the shadows were beginning to get longer.
Soon it would be dusk.

The old man was waiting
at the door of the theatre.
His wrinkled, monkey face
lit up at the sight of them.
'Come in, come in,
sit wherever you like!'

The theatre was completely empty.
'Isn't anyone else coming?'
asked Jenny's mother.

'Doesn't look like it!'
said the old man, with a laugh.
'Never mind, never mind!
The show must go on.'

He disappeared behind the curtain.
The lights went down.
Slow, sad organ music began to play.
It gave Jenny a spooky feeling.
What was going to happen?

6

A Sad Story

The curtains opened.
The General and his wife
were standing on the stage.
There was no sign of the old man.
He must be behind the screen at the back.

The play was a sad one.
Jenny wasn't sure if she liked it.
There was something a bit strange about it.
Something a bit nasty.

The General and Lady Muck
were arguing about their son.
He should go to war, said the General.
It would make a man of him.

No, said Lady Muck. He should marry
his nice young girlfriend and settle down.

The General got very angry.
The dog came on and the General kicked it.
It howled with pain and ran off.

Johnny came on singing a song
about being in love.
The General hit him.
Then Lady Muck hit the General.

The dog came back
with a letter in its mouth.
Johnny read it and burst into tears.
Sweetheart was dead.

Johnny went off to fight in the war.
He came home covered in blood
and died in his father's arms.

The dog howled with grief.
The General kicked it.
It bit him.
The General shot it.
Then he died of the bite.
And Lady Muck died of grief.

It was a silly story.
Yet somehow, you couldn't laugh at it.
The little puppets looked alive.
They looked like real people.

At the end, the puppets all got up
and danced a horrible dance.
The slow, sad organ music played.
The puppets bowed.
Then the curtains closed.

Jenny and her parents clapped.
The old man came out from behind the
curtain.
'Did you like it?' he asked.
'It looked ever so real,' said Jenny.
'But it was very sad.'

'I need a puppet to play Sweetheart,
that's the trouble,' said the old man.
'Then I could put a nice love scene in.'

'Good night,' said Jenny's Dad.

It was dark when they got outside.

'Horrible!' said Jenny's mother.
'I expect it will give us all nightmares.'

'It was only a puppet show!' said Jenny.
'It won't give me nightmares.'
But she was wrong.

7

Bad Dreams

Jenny dreamed the door of her bedroom opened.
The puppets came in and stood by the bed.
The moonlight shone on their faces.
They were smiling.

'My Sweetheart!' said Johnny. 'My love!
Come away with us.'

Jenny opened her mouth to say
that she was not his Sweetheart.
But she could not speak.

Johnny held out his hand.
Jenny took it and got out of bed.
She couldn't help herself.
Lady Muck took her other hand.
They led her out of the room
and down the stairs.
The General walked in front,
the dog walked behind.

They led her through the moonlit streets.
The puppets were only small,
no bigger than two-year-olds.
But Jenny could not break away.
She had to go with them.

They reached the little theatre.
The General reached up and opened the door.

'You're going to be my wife, Sweetheart,'
said Johnny.
'And we'll be together for ever
and ever and ever!'

Jenny opened her mouth to scream.
But no sound came out.

Then she woke up.
The puppets were gone.
She was standing alone
in the little dark puppet theatre.

She had been sleepwalking.

8

'Hello, Sweetheart'

The lights came on.
Music began to play.
The curtains opened.
The four puppets came on stage.
They bowed to Jenny
and began to dance.
They danced slowly,
lifting their arms and legs up high.
Their painted faces smiled at Jenny.

Jenny was badly frightened.
But if the puppets were dancing,
the old man must be there,
pulling the strings.
Perhaps he would help her.
Perhaps he would take her home.
She called out.

'Excuse me!
Are you there?'

The old man came out
from behind the stage.
He walked towards Jenny.
He was grinning all over his monkey face.
'Hello, Sweetheart.
How nice to see you!'

But Jenny didn't answer.
She stared past him at the stage.
The puppets were still dancing.

9

'I want to go home'

Jenny managed to speak.
'They ... they're dancing
on their own!'

'Yes, I've got them very well trained,'
said the old man.
'I don't need to pull the strings for them now.
They know what they must do.
Of course, it will be different for you
at first, Sweetheart.

I'll have to pull your strings.
Until I've got you trained.'

'I want to go home,' said Jenny.

The old man shook his head gently.
'Oh no,' he said.
'You won't be going home again.
You belong to me now, Sweetheart.'

'Don't call me Sweetheart!' said Jenny.
She turned to go.
Quick as a monkey,
the old man put his hand on top of her head
and pressed down.

Something very strange happened.
Jenny felt herself getting shorter
and shorter – as though she was sinking
through the floor.
Soon, she was only as big
as a two-year-old child.

The old man raised his hand.
Jenny raised hers too, without wanting to.
She saw that there was a string
fixed to her hand
and the old man was holding it.
There were strings on her other hand and her
head and her feet, too.

'Come, Sweetheart, let's dance!'
said the old man.
He led her towards the stage.

The other puppets smiled at her.
Jenny wanted to scream, to cry out,
but a smile was fixed to her face too.
She joined in the dance,
lifting her arms and legs up high.